The Golden Years of Irving Berlin

Design: PETER WHITE
Editorial: EDWARD LEA
Picture Research: NICOLAS NACHT
Photographic Prints: NATIONAL FILM ARCHIVE

The Golden Years of Irving Berlin

A BIOGRAPHICAL SKETCH OF IRVING BERLIN

"When at last the composer of the great American opera sets out to find a libretto he might look further but fare worse than Berlin's own story," was how Jerome Kern summed up the life of his friend and contemporary.

Although Irving Berlin has been a leading name in popular music longer than any other twentieth century songwriter, he was originally called Israel Baline. One of eight children, he was born on 11 May 1888 to Moses and Leah Lipkin Baline in Temun, Siberian Russia. When the Czar's soldiers began their pogroms, the Balines—all but two of the older children—fled to the Promised Land of America.

In 1892 they settled in New York's East side and for the next eight years Moses Baline struggled to support his family, earning a meagre income supervising kosher meats. He supplemented his earnings by giving Hebrew lessons to children and occasionally serving as cantor in the local synagogue. The young Israel, had a pleasant voice and enjoyed nothing better than to sing with his father in the choir. On his way to and from school he also heard the varied songs of the cosmopolitan community.

When Moses Baline died only four years after arriving in the New World his eight-year-old son Izzy had to help with the family finances by selling newspapers in the streets. From the doorways of the many Lower East Side saloons he was to hear the waiters who served drinks singing the popular songs of the day.

At the age of fourteen he ran away from home and made a living as best he could. Sometimes he sang with "Blind Sol," a street singer who wandered from bar to bar. For a time he found work as a song-plugger for Harry Von Tilzer. Then in 1906 he was offered his first permanent job as a singing waiter at Pelham's Cafe, run by 'Nigger' Mike Salter.

It was through the waiters at a nearby café writing a hit song that Izzy Baline acquired a new name and had his first song published. 'Nigger' Mike was so annoyed at the publicity enjoyed by the rival café that he instructed his singing waiter to concoct a song that would advertise Pelham's. Izzy collaborated with fellow waiter Nick Nicholson and 'Marie From Sunny Italy' was the result, a song that earned him only thirty-seven cents at the time. On the front cover of the sheet music was printed, "Words by I. Berlin, Music by M. Nicholson."

When Irving Berlin left Pelham's he moved uptown to Kelly's Saloon in Union Square. Here he was hired by a customer who had a vaudeville act to write a topical verse. Berlin picked on the story of Dorando, a marathon runner who was disqualified in the 1908 London Olympic Games through being "helped" to victory by spectators agonising over his near exhaustion. The vaudervillian never used the verse so Berlin tried to market it as a song lyric.

Ted Snyder, a young composer-publisher, who had recently formed his own music company, was impressed by 'Dorando,' assumed that Berlin had a melody and after accepting the song referred him to the staff pianist and arranger. 'Dorando' not only helped Berlin to establish a link between himself and Snyder; it forced him to improvise and dictate his first but perfectly serviceable melody to the arranger.

He was offered a permanent job by Snyder as a staff songwriter with a twenty-five dollars weekly drawing allowance against future royalties. For the next few years he was to write mainly words—Snyder or other composers supplied the melodies—for dozens of songs.

His first genuine successes were 'Sadie Salome, Go Home,' 'My Wife's Gone To The Country' and 'That Mesmerising Mendelssohn Tune,' which he based on Mendelssohn's 'Spring Song.'

In 1911 came what has been called his most colourful achievement 'Alexander's Ragtime Band,' which had a strong influence on contemporary composers. People the world over were captivated by its original freshness and irresistible vitality and behaved as if Berlin had just invented 'rag' music. Ragtime had emerged in the late nineteenth century but it was Berlin, who made it universally popular with 'Alexander.' It was by no means his first ragtime song but more than any other single number it made Tin Pan Alley's sentimental love ballads take a secondary place. As has often been pointed out, 'Alexander's Ragtime Band' itself contains little syncopation and is more a song *about* ragtime than a ragtime song. Nevertheless, it was Irving Berlin himself who was the most significant contributor to the tide of ragtime songs which followed. In the same year came 'That Mysterious Rag,' 'Ragtime Violin' and 'Everybody's Doin' It.'

Billed as "The Ragtime King," Berlin played one week in 1913 at the London Hippodrome where the audience appeared to believe that he was responsible for every ragtime song ever written.

Nearly all Berlin's early work was along the lines of comedy or ragtime. It was only when tragedy came into his life that he turned to ballads which eventually proved to be his greatest successes.

He had married in 1912, Dorothy Goetz, the attractive sister of Broadway producer Ray Goetz. The Berlins spent their honeymoon in Cuba. On their return to New York the bride suddenly became ill and died within a short time, having contracted typhoid fever. Shocked into despair, Berlin expressed himself in the ballad, 'When I Lost You.' It was the first time he had commented on his own emotions and the public responded by making the song an enormous hit, although it was obviously written with no commercial reward in mind.

At the age of 26 Irving Berlin wrote his first complete score for Broadway, "Watch your Step," which included 'Play A Simple Melody,' the first of the "double melodies" that have become his trademark. The following year, 1915, "Stop! Look! Listen!"

contained 'I Love A Piano,' clearly a labour of love, in another all-Berlin score.

In the First World War he was called into uniform and stationed at Camp Upton, Fort Yaphank, Long Island, where, in his own words, he "wasn't much of a soldier." He hated getting up at 5 a.m. and suggested to General Bell that with all the talent in the Army he might be allowed to get an all-soldier show together to aid recruitment and boost morale. "Yip, Yip, Yaphank" eventually played to 'House Full' notices on Broadway, bringing in a lot of revenue to the army and adding to the growing repertory of Berlin hits with 'Mandy' and 'Oh, How I Hate To Get Up In The Morning.' Berlin's pre-war practice of working through the night and sleeping till mid-day gave him heart for the latter tuneful effort, which he sang again in his Second World War all-soldier show, "This Is The Army."

After the war in 1919, Irving Berlin formed his own publishing company. As a songwriter he was as prolific as ever and in the same year was commissioned to write the score for "The Ziegfeld Follies." One of the songs, 'A Pretty Girl Is Like A Melody,' with its pure, uncontrived melody became the theme song for "The Ziegfeld Follies" and countless subsequent fashion shows and beauty contests.

In 1921 Berlin made a bid to rival the great Ziegfeld himself by opening his own theatre, The Music Box, a venture he suggested and executed with the help of veteran showmen Sam Harris and Joseph Schenck. Berlin wrote a theme for his new theatre, 'Say It With Music,' which he included in the first of the opulent and lavish "Music Box Revues."

After Berlin met and fell in love with the beautiful and talented Ellin Mackay he began writing some of his most celebrated waltz songs, such as 'What'll I Do?', 'Remember,' and 'All Alone.' She was the daughter of the wealthy businessman Clarence Mackay. He was bitterly opposed to the union between his socialite daughter and a mere songwriter and used every resource at his command to break up the affair.

America's favourite rags to riches story was realised when Ellin defied parental approval and married Irving, who made her a wedding present of 'Always,' his most popular waltz song. The marriage was entirely successful despite Charles Mackay's objections. It was to be some years before father and daughter became reconciled.

Inexplicably, after he had written yet another waltz hit, 'The Song Is Ended' in 1927, Berlin reached what was for him an arid creative period. He became convinced that his reservoir of song ideas had run dry and he lost confidence in himself. For several years he wrote fewer songs and little that he considered of value. This was the period of the great Depression and Berlin also became a victim of the economic crisis.

Then in 1932 "Face The Music" revealed that Irving Berlin was back in form. This musical comedy peppered with satirical allusions to the Depression contained one of his most enduring ballads, 'Soft Lights and Sweet Music.' The same year saw the publication of 'How Deep Is The Ocean' and 'Say It Isn't So.'

The topical revue "As Thousands Cheer" included a tune he had discarded years before because of a weak lyric. With new words and a slightly changed melody 'Smile And Show Your Dimple' became 'Easter Parade,' 'the official song of Easter.' Other outstanding numbers were 'Heat Wave' and 'Not For All The Rice In China.'

By 1935 Berlin was working in Hollywood and for the next four years was primarily a film-song composer. "Top Hat" was specially tailored for Fred Astaire and Ginger Rogers. Berlin himself said of Astaire, "He's a real inspiration for a writer." He added that he would never have written 'Top Hat, White Tie And Tails,' 'Cheek To Cheek,' or 'Isn't This A Lovely Day?' if he hadn't had Astaire and Rogers to write for.

Ginger Rogers in an interview returned the compliment: "I think he's sort of the apple pie type of composer that makes you want to stand up and bleat out a song whether you can sing or not. He writes that type of song."

In 1939 Berlin brought out of his trunk a song that he had discarded twenty years before. Kate Smith was the singer who introduced the song that has become "the second National Anthem of the United States," 'God Bless America.' Berlin voluntarily signed over all royalties to the Boy Scouts and Girl Guides of America.

With the smash-hit musical, "Louisiana Purchase," which ran for 444 performances, Irving Berlin returned to Broadway in 1940. The principal song was 'It's A Lovely Day Tomorrow' and the pure, hymn-like melody and optimistic lyric appealed to a world being drawn into war, showing again Berlin's instinctive awareness of public taste.

Soon after the Japanese attacked Pearl Harbour, he recognised the need for a new all-army show to boost morale. "This Is The Army" was even more successful in the Second World War than "Yip, Yip, Yaphank" had been in the First, all profits going to the service charity, Army Emergency Relief. The show was made into a motion picture, then crossed the Atlantic, playing at the London Palladium for two weeks and touring for seven months in the United Kingdom and Ireland. Before its final performance in 1945 the show visited Italy, Africa, Australia and various bases in the South Pacific. Berlin himself appeared with the Company for about three years.

In 1942 Irving Berlin surpassed himself once again with the film "Holiday Inn," starring Bing Crosby and Fred Astaire. It was the story of a man who was lazy who only wanted to work on holidays, so he opened an Inn. 'White Christmas' took on a meaning that the composer says he never intended and it became a peace song in the midst of war. It won not only an Academy Award; the sales figures are unequalled by any other American song and it is now a permanent part of the Christmas festivities.

Berlin's other successful films of the 1940s were "Blue Skies" (1946), also starring Bing Crosby and Fred Astaire, and "Easter Parade" in which Judy Garland and Fred Astaire introduced the comedy classic, 'A Couple Of Swells.'

His most important musical comedy is generally considered to be "Annie Get Your Gun." As is well known, Jerome Kern was commissioned to write the score. After Kern's tragic death in 1945, Irving Berlin was called in and eventually agreed to write the songs. He has said that he felt uneasy about trying to step into Kern's shoes, yet in a short time he was to write a score that contained a dozen legitimate hits, ranging from the comic and satirical to the tender and sentimental. They include, 'Doin' What Comes Natur'lly,' 'You Can't Get A Man With A Gun,' 'Anything You Can Do,' 'The Girl That I Marry,' 'They Say It's Wonderful' and that "national anthem of the theatre" 'There's No Business Like Show Business.'

Musicals following "Annie" have added to the stockpile of memorable Berlin songs. "Miss Liberty" opened on Broadway in 1949 and ran for 308 performances. "Call Me Madam," starring Ethel Merman who also appeared in the film version, includes 'It's A Lovely Day Today,' 'Marrying For Love' and 'You're Just In Love.' This last song makes contrapuntal use of two melodies and two lyrics as in the earlier 'Play A Simple Melody.' A similar kind of song, 'Empty Pockets Filled With Love,' appeared in Berlin's 1962 Broaway show, "Mr President." For the 1966 revival of "Annie Get Your Gun" he wrote yet another "double song", 'An Old Fashioned Wedding.'

In recent years, Irving Berlin's main interest outside his music is his family and the small circle of friends with whom he keeps in touch by telephone. He has three daughters and nine grandchildren. His main hobby is painting pictures which are naive in style, often humorous and completely charming. He loves having his family around him either at his fashionable apartment in New York or at his fifty-acre farm in the Catskill Mountains.

The Smithsonian Institution in Washington was presented by Irving Berlin in December 1972 with an upright piano. As Berlin's piano technique was limited and he was restricted to playing mainly on the black keys in F sharp this was one of two pianos he had fitted with an ingenious mechanism. When he moved a lever it was capable of shifting the entire keyboard and transposing the piece he was playing into the required tonality. Too much however, has been made of Berlin's limited technical accomplishments. Many trained musicians he has worked with have given testimony to the fact that he has an extraordinary feeling for melody, harmony and form with a rare instinct for the perfect combination of text and tune. A talent peculiarly his own was his gift for styling a song to suit a particular entertainer's abilities.

He has been called "the most successful songwriter of all time." Certainly, he has had an almost uncanny awareness of popular taste, which has won the admiration of his peers. George Gershwin was a sincere devotee and named him "America's Schubert." Jerome Kern, when asked at a dinner in London, what were the chief characteristics of the American nation replied that the average United States citizen was perfectly epitomised by Irving Berlin's music. "Irving Berlin has *no* place in American music—he *is* American music."

NOTES ON THE SONGS
The performers of the songs are indicated by the letters in brackets

"WATCH YOUR STEP" (Revue)
New York (New Amsterdam Theatre) 8 December. Cast included:
Vernon and Irene Castle, Charles King, Frank Tinney, Elizabeth Brice
London (Empire Theatre) 4 May 1915. Cast included: Ethel Levey, Joseph Coyne, Lupino Lane
PLAY A SIMPLE MELODY
(hit records made by Bing Crosby, Ethel Merman and Jean Sablon)

"THE ZIEGFELD FOLLIES OF 1919" (Revue)
New York (New Amsterdam Theatre) 16 June 1919. Cast included:
Marilyn Miller, Eddie Cantor, John Steel (a)
A PRETTY GIRL IS LIKE A MELODY (a)
(see also "The Great Ziegfeld" 1936 Film)

"THE ZIEGFELD FOLLIES OF 1927" (Revue)
New York (New Amsterdam Theatre) 16 August 1927. Cast included:
Eddie Cantor, Ruth Etting (a), The Brox Sisters, Andrew Toombes
SHAKING THE BLUES AWAY (a)

"TOP HAT" (RKO 1935)
Fred Astaire (a) Ginger Rogers (b), Helen Broderick, Edward Everett Horton, Eric Blore, Erik Rhodes
CHEEK TO CHEEK (a-b)
ISN'T THIS A LOVELY DAY? (a-b)
NO STRINGS (a)
TOP HAT, WHITE TIE AND TAILS (a)

"FOLLOW THE FLEET" (RKO 1936)
Fred Astaire (a) Ginger Rogers (b) Harriet Hilliard, Randolph Scott, Lucille Ball, Betty Grable, Tony Martin
I'M PUTTING ALL MY EGGS IN ONE BASKET (a-b)
LET'S FACE THE MUSIC AND DANCE (a-b)
LET YOURSELF GO (a-b)
WE SAW THE SEA (a & Chorus)

"THE GREAT ZIEGFELD" (MGM 1936)
William Powell, Luise Rainer, Myrna Loy, Fanny Brice, Virginia Bruce, Ray Bolger, Dennis Morgan
A PRETTY GIRL IS LIKE A MELODY (a)
(originally in "Ziegfeld Follies of 1919")

"ON THE AVENUE" (Fox 1937)
Dick Powell (a) Alice Faye (b) E E Clive (c) The Ritz Brothers, Jean Davies, Madeleine Carroll, Walter Catlett
I'VE GOT MY LOVE TO KEEP ME WARM (a-b-c)

"CAREFREE" (RKO 1938)
Fred Astaire (a) Ginger Rogers (b) Ralph Bellamy, Jack Carson, Luella Gear, Clarence Kolb
CHANGE PARTNERS (a-b)

"LOUISIANA PURCHASE" (Musical Comedy)
New York (Imperial Theatre) 28 May 1940. Cast included: Victor Moore, Vera Zorina, William Gaxton, Irene Bordoni (a)
IT'S A LOVELY DAY TOMORROW (a)

"HOLIDAY INN" (Paramount 1942)
Bing Crosby (a) Fred Astaire (b) Marjorie Reynolds (c) Virginia Dale, Louise Beavers, Walter Abel
BE CAREFUL, IT'S MY HEART (a-b-c)
WHITE CHRISTMAS (a-c)

"THIS IS THE ARMY" (Revue)
New York (Broadway Theatre) 4 July 1942. Cast included: Ezra Stone, William Horne, Jules Oshins, Irving Berlin
London (Palladium) 10 November 1943. "This Is The Army" Revue Company. Film (Warner/1st National) 1943: Kate Smith, Irving Berlin, Joan Leslie, George Murphy, Frances Langford, Gertrude Niesen, Ronald Reagan, Joe Louis, "This Is The Army" Revue Company (a)
THIS IS THE ARMY, MISTER JONES (a)

"ANNIE GET YOUR GUN" (Musical Comedy & Film)
New York (Imperial Theatre) 16 May 1946. Cast included: Ethel Merman, Ray Middleton.
London (Coliseum) 7 June 1947. Cast included: Dolores Gray, Bill Johnson. Film (MGM) 1949: Betty Hutton (a), Howard Keel (b), Keenan Wynn (c), Louis Calhern (d)
ANYTHING YOU CAN DO (a & b)
DOIN' WHAT COMES NATUR'LLY (a)
I GOT THE SUN IN THE MORNING (a)
I'M AN INDIAN TOO (a)
MY DEFENCES ARE DOWN (b)
YOU CAN'T GET A MAN WITH A GUN (a)
THERE'S NO BUSINESS LIKE SHOW BUSINESS (a-b-c-d)
THEY SAY IT'S WONDERFUL (a-b)
THE GIRL THAT I MARRY (b)

"EASTER PARADE" (MGM 1948)
Fred Astaire (a) Judy Garland (b) Peter Lawford (c) Ann Miller (d) Dick Beavers, Jules Munshin, Clinton Sundberg
A COUPLE OF SWELLS (a-b)
EASTER PARADE (a-b)
(originally in "As Thousands Cheer" 1933; "Stop Press" in UK)
A FELLA WITH AN UMBRELLA (b-c)
I LOVE A PIANO (a-b)
(originally in "Stop! Look! Listen!" (Revue 1915))
STEPPIN' OUT WITH MY BABY (a)
SHAKING THE BLUES AWAY (d)
(Originally in "The Ziegfeld Follies Of 1927")

"CALL ME MADAM" (Musical Comedy & Film)
New York (Imperial Theatre) 12 October 1950. Cast included:
Ethel Merman, Russell Nype, Paul Lukas
London (Coliseum) 15 March 1952. Cast included: Billie Worth, Anton Walbrook, Shani Wallis, Jeff Warren
Film (Fox) 1953: Ethel Merman (a), George Sanders (b), Donald O'Connor (c), Vera-Ellen (d) (dubbed by Carole Richards), Billy De Wolfe
IT'S A LOVELY DAY TODAY (c-d)
MARRYING FOR LOVE (b)
YOU'RE JUST IN LOVE (a-b-c)

"WHITE CHRISTMAS" (Paramount 1954)
Bing Crosby (a) Danny Kaye (b) Rosemary Clooney (c) Vera-Ellen (d) (dubbed by Trudy Stevens), Dean Jagger, Mary Wickes
COUNT YOUR BLESSINGS INSTEAD OF SHEEP (a-c)
SISTERS (a-b-c-d)

"THERE'S NO BUSINESS LIKE SHOW BUSINESS" (Fox 1954)
Ethel Merman, Dan Dailey, Mitzi Gaynor, Donald O'Connor, Johnny Ray (a), Marilyn Monroe (b)
HEAT WAVE (b)
(originally in "As Thousands Cheer" 1933)
IF YOU BELIEVE (a)
(Written in 1940)

Fred Astaire in "Top Hat" (RKO 1935)

Ginger Rogers & Fred Astaire in "Follow The Fleet" (RKO 1936)

Dick Powell & Madeleine Carroll in "On The Avenue" (20th Century Fox 1937)

Ginger Rogers & Fred Astaire in "Carefree" (RKO 1938)

Bing Crosby & Marjorie Reynolds in "Holiday Inn" (Paramount 1942)

Irving Berlin & Chorus in "This Is The Army" (Warner Bros. 1943)

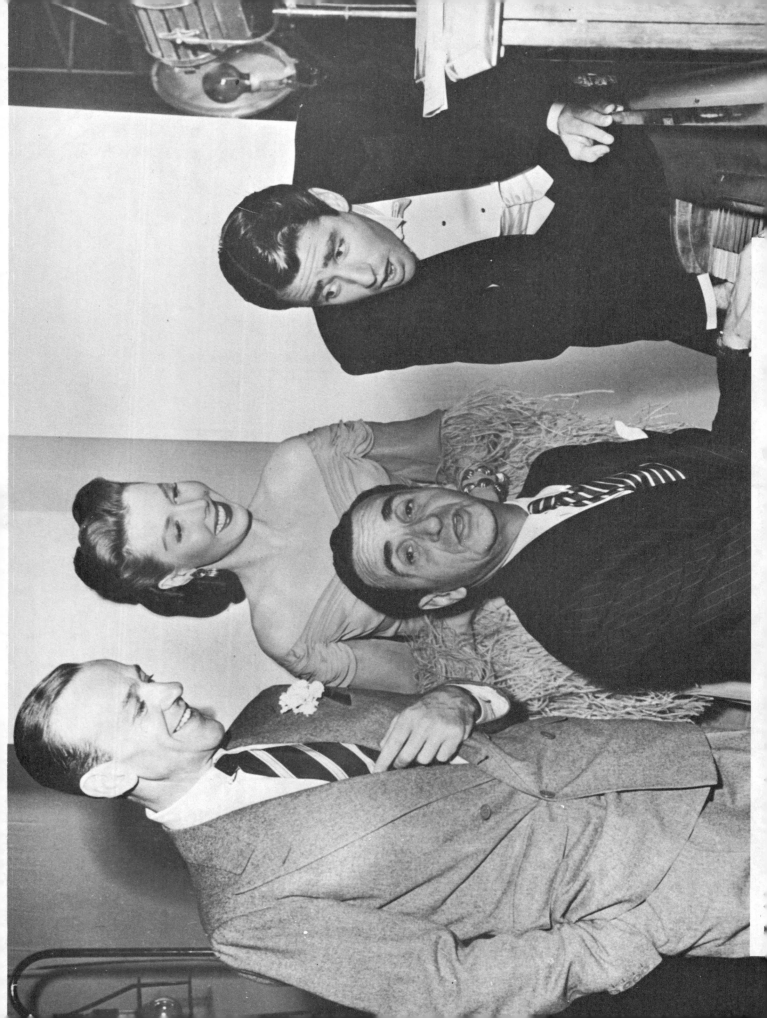

Fred Astaire & Judy Garland in "Easter Parade" (MGM 1948)

Ann Miller & Fred Astaire in "Easter Parade" (MGM 1948)

Ethel Merman & Donald O'Connor in "Call Me Madam" (20th Century Fox 1959)

Rosemary Clooney & Vera-Ellen in "White Christmas" (Paramount 1954)

Marilyn Monroe in "There's No Business Like Show Business" (20th Century Fox 1954)

PLAY A SIMPLE MELODY

Words and Music by
IRVING BERLIN

DUET

Mus-i-cal de-mon, set your honey a dreamin' Won't you play me some rag.   Just change that clas-i-cal nag

Won't   you   play a sim-ple   mel - o - dy   Like   my

Eb   Bb7   Eb   Gbdim   Bb7

to some sweet beau-ti-ful drag.   If you will play from a cop-y of a tune that is chop-py, You'll get

moth-er sang to me._____   One   with good old fash-ioned

Bb7aug Eb   Ebdim   Bb7   Fm7 Bb7 Eb   Bb7   Eb   Gbdim

all my ap-plause   And that is sim-ply be-cause   I want to lis-ten to rag._____

har - mo-ny.   Play   a sim - ple mel - o - dy._____

Bb7   Eb Eb7 Ebdim Abm Eb

SHAKING THE BLUES AWAY

Words and Music by
IRVING BERLIN

A PRETTY GIRL IS LIKE A MELODY

Words and Music by
IRVING BERLIN

REFRAIN

CHEEK TO CHEEK

Words and Music by
IRVING BERLIN

ISN'T THIS A LOVELY DAY?

Words and Music by
IRVING BERLIN

The weather is fright'ning; The thunder and light-ning Seem to be hav-ing their way. But as far as I'm con-cerned, it's a love-ly day. The turn in the weather will keep us to-geth-er, So I can hon-est-ly say That as far as I'm con-

CHORUS

NO STRINGS

Words and Music by
IRVING BERLIN

I wake up ev'ry morning with a smile on my face, Ev'ry-thing in its place as it should be. I start out ev'ry morning just as free as the breeze, My cares up-on the shelf, Be-cause I find my-self with—

CHORUS

TOP HAT, WHITE TIE AND TAILS

Words and Music by
IRVING BERLIN

LET'S FACE THE MUSIC AND DANCE

Words and Music by
IRVING BERLIN

LET YOURSELF GO

Words and Music by
IRVING BERLIN

CHORUS

WE SAW THE SEA

Words and Music by
IRVING BERLIN

48

I'M PUTTING ALL MY EGGS IN ONE BASKET

Words and Music by
IRVING BERLIN

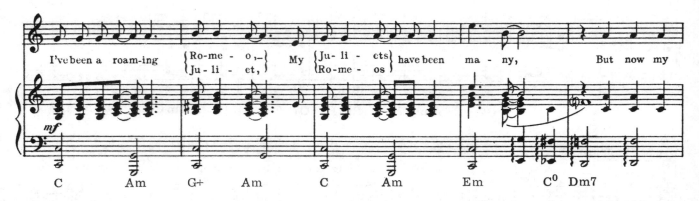

I've been a roam-ing {Ro-me-o,— / Ju-li-et,} My {Ju-li-ets / Ro-me-os} have been ma-ny, But now my

roam-ing days have gone._____ Too ma-ny i-rons in the fire,— Is

worse than not hav-ing a-ny. I've had my share and from now on:_____

CHORUS

I'VE GOT MY LOVE TO KEEP ME WARM

Words and Music by
IRVING BERLIN

CHANGE PARTNERS

Words and Music by
IRVING BERLIN

55

IT'S A LOVELY DAY TOMORROW

Words and Music by
IRVING BERLIN

BE CAREFUL, IT'S MY HEART

Words and Music by
IRVING BERLIN

WHITE CHRISTMAS

Words & Music by
IRVING BERLIN

THIS IS THE ARMY, MISTER JONES

Words and Music by
IRVING BERLIN

ANYTHING YOU CAN DO

Words and Music by
IRVING BERLIN

DOIN' WHAT COMES NATUR'LLY

Words and Music by
IRVING BERLIN

I GOT THE SUN IN THE MORNING

Words and Music by
IRVING BERLIN

MY DEFENCES ARE DOWN

Words and Music by
IRVING BERLIN

YOU CAN'T GET A MAN WITH A GUN

Words and Music by
IRVING BERLIN

THERE'S NO BUSINESS LIKE SHOW BUSINESS

Words and Music by
IRVING BERLIN

REFRAIN

REFRAIN

THEY SAY IT'S WONDERFUL

Words and Music by
IRVING BERLIN

THE GIRL THAT I MARRY

Words and Music by
IRVING BERLIN

92

EASTER PARADE

Words and Music by
IRVING BERLIN

Nev-er saw you look Quite so pret-ty be - fore,_____ Nev-er

saw you dressed Quite so love-ly; what's more _____ I could

hard-ly wait To keep our date This love-ly East-er morn-ing, And my

heart beat fast As I came through the door— for;

REFRAIN

In your East - er bon - net With all the frills up - on it, You'll

be the grand - est la - dy in the East - er Par - ade.

I'll be all in clov - er, And when they look you ov - er I'll

be the proud - est fel - low in the East - er Par - ade. To the

A FELLA WITH AN UMBRELLA

Words and Music by
IRVING BERLIN

I LOVE A PIANO

Words and Music by
IRVING BERLIN

A COUPLE OF SWELLS

Words and Music by
IRVING BERLIN

REFRAIN

We would drive up the Av-en-ue, but we have-n't got the price. We would skate up the
We would sail up the Av-en-ue, but we have-n't got a yacht. We would drive up the

Dm7 G7 C Cmaj7 C6 Am7 Dm7 D7 G7 Dm7 G7 C Cmaj7

Av-en-ue, but there is-n't an-y ice. We would ride on a bi-cy-cle, but we
Av-en-ue, but the horse we had was shot. We would ride on a trolley car, but we

C6 Am7 Cm D7 G7 F#dim G7 C E7aug F F#dim

have-n't got a bike. So we'll walk up the Av-en-ue. Yes, we'll walk up the
have-n't got the fare. So we'll walk up the Av-en-ue. Yes, we'll walk up the

C C#dim Dm7 G7 C Ebdim Dm7

1
2

Av-en-ue, And to walk up the Av-en-ue's what we like._____ like._____
Av-en-ue, Yes, we'll walk up the Av-en-ue 'til we're there._____ there._____

D7 G7 Dm7 G7 C Am7 Fmaj7 G7 C F C

STEPPIN' OUT WITH MY BABY

Words and Music by
IRVING BERLIN

108

MARRYING FOR LOVE

Words and Music by
IRVING BERLIN

110

YOU'RE JUST IN LOVE

Words and Music by
IRVING BERLIN

HEAT WAVE

Words and Music by
IRVING BERLIN

116

118

IT'S A LOVELY DAY TODAY

Words and Music by
IRVING BERLIN

COUNT YOUR BLESSINGS INSTEAD OF SHEEP

Words and Music by
IRVING BERLIN

SISTERS

Words and Music by
IRVING BERLIN

125

IF YOU BELIEVE

Words and Music by
IRVING BERLIN

Moderato *(With expression)*

IF YOU BE-LIEVE __ that there's a heav-en __ you'll get to heav-en __

F   Bb Bbm   F   Dm   G9   G7

__ IF YOU BE-LIEVE __ IF YOU BE-LIEVE that there are

C11 C7   F   C7   F

an - gels __ you'll see the an - gels __ IF YOU BE-LIEVE __

Bb Bbm   F   Dm   G9   G7   C11 C7   F   Gm7 F⁰ F